Quick Quiz 2

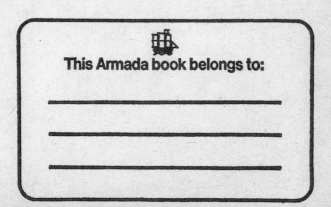

This Armada book belongs to:

Also in Armada

Quick Quiz
Armada Quiz and Puzzle Book No. 8
Armada Crossword Books 1 - 17
Football Quiz 1982/83
Calculator Fun and Games
The Whizzkid's Handbook
The Whizzkid's Handbook 2
The Trickster's Handbook
The Secret Agent's Handbook
The Millionaire's Handbook
The Explorer's Handbook
The Alien Spotter's Handbook
The Awful Joke Book
The Even More Awful Joke Book

Simon Reed

QUICK QUIZ 2
Illustrations by Neil Miles

 with faces by Harry Hargreaves

Armada

Quick Quiz 2 was first published in Armada in 1983
by Fontana Paperbacks,
8 Grafton Street, London W1X 3LA.

Printed in Great Britain by
William Collins Sons & Co. Ltd., Glasgow

Before you start . . .

There are three types of *Quick Quiz* in this book:
General Quizzes, Picture Quizzes and Subject Quizzes.
Every question has a quick answer, and all except the
Picture Quizzes can be read aloud, so you'll find this
book useful for sessions of "Junior Mastermind" or
family General Knowledge games. Teachers can use
Quick Quiz, too, for some fun in the classroom.

The 25 *General Quizzes* get more difficult as they go
along. You may think No. 1 is pretty easy, but by the
time you get to No. 15 you might find yourself chewing
the end of your pencil . . . and anyone who can get full
marks for No. 25 must be a walking encyclopaedia!

Most of the *Picture Quizzes* have a list of answers printed
underneath. To do these quizzes the easy way, simply
match the words to the pictures. However, if you prefer
to make life more difficult for yourself, just cover up the
bottom of the page.

To answer the *Subject Quizzes*, you don't have to be a
genius in any particular field, though you're bound to
find some easier than others, of course.

Set yourself time limits, if you like, or see if you can beat
your own record. Have a race with your friends, and see
who is the Quickest Quizzer. Ready . . . ? Steady . . . ? —
Go!

General Quiz . . .

1. Which fictional character is known as 007? .....
   James Bond. ✓

2. How many legs has a tripod? ... THREE ... ✓

3. Who was Robinson Crusoe's loyal servant? .....
   MAN FRIDAY ✓

4. What relation is your mother's brother to you?
   UNCLE ✓

5. Neil Armstrong was the first man to walk on the . . . what?
   THE MOON ✓

6. Which animal "never forgets"? Elephant ✓

7. Clubs, hearts, diamonds — what's missing?
   Spades ✓

8. What is the main ingredient of omelettes?
   eggs ✓

9. Which plant is the emblem of Scotland? ....
   Thistle. ✓

10. Whom does Wurzel Gummidge love? ? Aunt x
    Sally

9/10

6

...No. 1

11. What is a Knickerbocker Glory usually served in?

Tall glass ✓

12. Which is the highest mountain in the world?

Everest ✓

13. A hornet is a large kind of ... what? wasp nest ✓

14. Which has a mane, a lion or a lioness? lion ✓

15. Who "picked a peck of pickled pepper"?

Peter Piper ✓

16. In which book did a little girl fall down a rabbit hole?

Alice in Wonderland ✓

17. Which of Robin Hood's companions was very tall and strong?

? Little John x

18. What lands at a heliport? helicopter ✓

19. Which bird lays its eggs in other birds' nests?

cuccoo ✓

20. Who was king of the Knights of the Round Table?

Cromwell x ARTHUR

8/10

Colours

1. If you mix yellow, red and blue together, what colour do you get?

   green x BROWN

2. Cobalt, sapphire and electric are all words used to describe . . . what colour?

   Blue ✓

3. Saffron is used as a dye. What colour does it produce?

   Yellow ✓

4. How many colours are there in a rainbow?

   7 ✓

5. If you were an albino, what colour would your hair be?

   White ✓

6. What colour can be "shocking"? PINK ✓

7. Tangerines, clementines and satsumas are all the same colour. What is it?

   ORange ✓

8. If something is verdant, what colour is it? ✓

   green

9. Cochineal is a red dye made from crushed . . . what?

   ? Insects x

10. What colour is Indian ink? Black ✓

8/10

Picture Quiz . . . Say Cheese!

Can you name these cheeses?

A BRIE ✓

B Stilton ✓

C Cheddar ✓

D Cottage cheese ✓

E GRUYERE ✓

F EDAM ✓

6/6.

STILTON   COTTAGE CHEESE   BRIE   GRUYERE
CHEDDAR   EDAM

General Quiz . . .

1. Which fruit grows in a vineyard? GRAPES ✓

2. How many commandments did God give to Moses?
   TEN ✓

3. To which part of the body is mascara applied?
   EYES ✓

4. A Manx cat does not have a . . . what? TAIL ✓

5. Which star of silent films dressed as a bowler-hatted tramp with a cane?
   ~~LAURA~~ Charlie Chaplin ✓

6. What is made in a brewery? BEER ✓

7. Which elephant has the smaller ears, the Indian or African?
   Indian ✓

8. On which date is April Fools' Day? FIRST ✓

9. What do the Chinese use instead of knives and forks?
   Chopsticks ✓

10. What do the letters P.T.O. mean? Please Turn Over ✓

11. In which city would you find the Eiffel Tower, the Arc de Triomphe and the Louvre?
    PARIS ✓

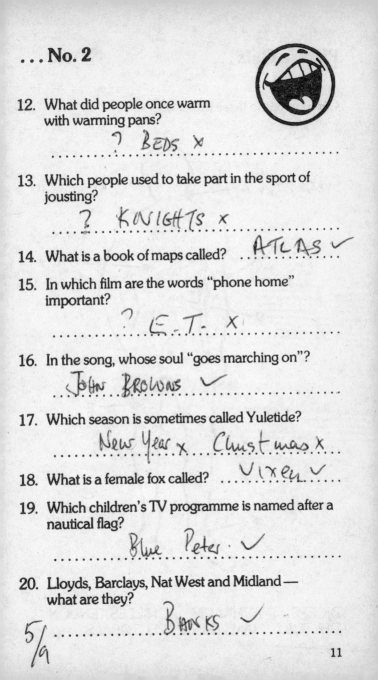

12. What did people once warm with warming pans?

    ? BEDS ✗

13. Which people used to take part in the sport of jousting?

    ? KNIGHTS ✗

14. What is a book of maps called? ...ATLAS ✓

15. In which film are the words "phone home" important?

    ? E.T. ✗

16. In the song, whose soul "goes marching on"?

    John BROWNS ✓

17. Which season is sometimes called Yuletide?

    New Year ✗ Christmas ✗

18. What is a female fox called? ...VIXEN ✓

19. Which children's TV programme is named after a nautical flag?

    Blue Peter ✓

20. Lloyds, Barclays, Nat West and Midland — what are they?

    BANKS ✓

5/9

Picture Quiz ...

Can you name these muscles?

Deltoid A

Biceps B ✓

C Pectorals

Diaphragm ✓ D

E Hamstring

Achilles Tendon F

4/6

BICEPS DIAPHRAGM ACHILLES TENDON
DELTOID HAMSTRING PECTORALS

... Inside You

... and these bones?

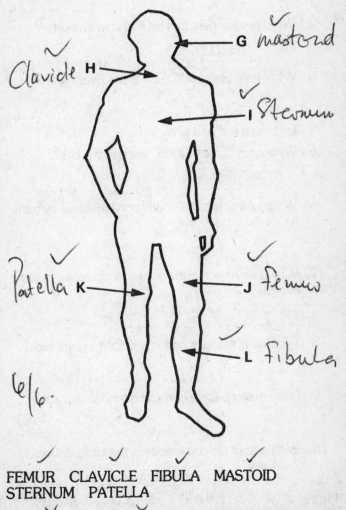

G mastoid ✓

Clavicle ✓ H →

I Sternum ✓

Patella ✓ K →

J femur ✓

L fibula ✓

6/6.

FEMUR ✓ CLAVICLE ✓ FIBULA ✓ MASTOID ✓
STERNUM ✓ PATELLA ✓

General Quiz . . .

1. Who travels through time in the "Tardis"?

   DR Who ✓

2. What kind of gem can be found in an oyster?

   Pearl - ✓

3. What nationality is "Dame Edna Everage"?

   Australian ~

4. Is claret a red or a white wine?   Red ✓

5. Who cries "Oyez! Oyez!" and rings a bell?

   Town Crier ✓

6. Which meat is traditionally accompanied by mint sauce?

   Lamb ✓

7. Which television artist created a character called Morph?

   Tony Hart ✓

8. What animals take part in a point-to-point race?

   ? Horses ✗

9. How many people can ride a tandem bicycle?

   Two ✓

10. With whom do you associate the exclamation "walkies!"?

    Barbara Woodhouse. ✓

9/10

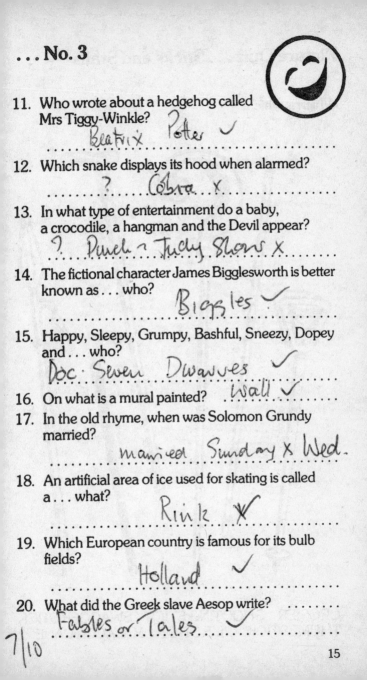

11. Who wrote about a hedgehog called
    Mrs Tiggy-Winkle?

    Beatrix Potter ✓

12. Which snake displays its hood when alarmed?

    ? Cobra ✗

13. In what type of entertainment do a baby,
    a crocodile, a hangman and the Devil appear?

    ? Punch n Judy Show ✗

14. The fictional character James Bigglesworth is better
    known as . . . who?

    Biggles ✓

15. Happy, Sleepy, Grumpy, Bashful, Sneezy, Dopey
    and . . . who?

    Doc. Seven Dwarves ✓

16. On what is a mural painted? *Wall* ✓

17. In the old rhyme, when was Solomon Grundy
    married?

    married Sunday ✗ *Wed.*

18. An artificial area of ice used for skating is called
    a . . . what?

    Rink ✗

19. Which European country is famous for its bulb
    fields?

    Holland ✓

20. What did the Greek slave Aesop write?

    Fables or Tales ✓

7/10

Picture Quiz . . . Sticks and Staffs

Which is which?

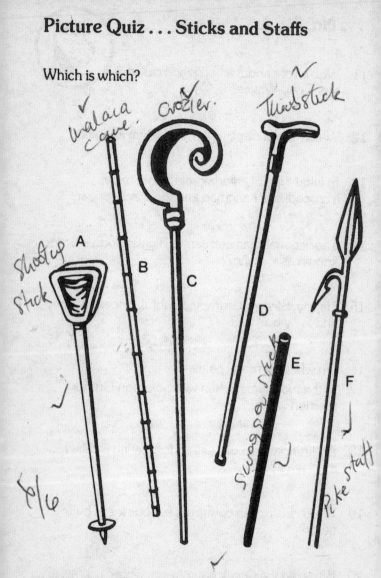

Malaca Cane ✓
Crozier. ✓
Thumbstick ✓
Shooting Stick
Swagger stick
Pike staff

A   B   C   D   E   F

**CROSIER   SHOOTING STICK   SWAGGER STICK
THUMBSTICK   PIKE STAFF   MALACCA CANE**

16

Gold and Silver

1. Everything he touched turned to gold. Who was he?

   ? King Midas x

2. Which film cowboy had a horse called Silver?

   Roy Rodgers x   Lone Ranger

3. Who broke a little bear's chair? *Red Riding Hood x*

4. "Every cloud has a silver . . ." — what?

   lining ✓

5. Is gold a hard or a soft metal? *Hard x Soft*

6. What name is given to a silver tray on which letters and cards are presented?

   Salver ✓

7. What is a dealer or worker in gold called?

   goldsmith ✓

8. Which tree has a silvery-white peeling bark?

   Birch ✓

9. What is the common name for a golden orfe?

   Ingot x — goldfish x

10. What make of car has a model called Silver Shadow?

    Rolls Royce ✓

5/10

General Quiz . . .

1. Which animal may be referred to as a "moggy"?

   Cat ✓

2. What instrument does James Galway play?

   Flute ✓

3. How many men did the Grand Old Duke of York command?

   Ten thousand Men ✓

4. What is scrumpy made from? ? Apples ✗

5. John Lennon, Paul McCartney, George Harrison and . . . who was the fourth Beatle?

   Ringo Starr ✓

6. What does a Sikh wear on his head? Turban ✓

7. In Mary Norton's books, who are the tiny people who live under floors?

   ? The Borrowers ✗

8. What is a fertile area in a desert called? Oasis ✓

9. Which TV entertainers use the expression "Fantabidozy"?

   The Krankies ✓

10. What was the name of Dick Turpin's horse?

    ? Black Bess

7/10

18

11. What type of building has sails? .... *Windmill* ✓

12. In which film and musical is an orphan adopted by Daddy Warbucks?

    .... *Annie* ✓

13. What parts of your body might suffer from callouses and bunions? ✓

    .... *Feet*

14. The five senses are: sight, hearing, smell, taste and ... what?

    .... *Touch* ✓

15. What food is traditionally eaten on Shrove Tuesday?

    Pancakes ✓

16. Is a carp a freshwater or seawater fish? ....

    .... *freshwater* ✓ ✓

17. What is a bachelor? .... *Unmarried man*

18. In which county is Norwich? .... *Norfolk* ✓

19. What are Canada's mounted policemen known as?

9/10 .... *Rockies*

20. What is grown in a paddy field? .... *Rice* ✓

19

Sweet Things

1. In *Hansel and Gretel*, what was the witch's house made of?

   liquorice X gingerbread X

2. A yam is a kind of sweet... what?   Potato ✓

3. What kind of food is sometimes described by the word "sweetmeal"?

   Biscuits. ✓

4. In which country is the Sugar Loaf Mountain? ✓

   S. America - (Texas) Brazil

5. At what age is a young girl often described as "sweet"?

   Sixteen ✓

6. What delicacy is made from whipped egg whites and sugar?

   Meringue ✓

7. Who, or what, are made of "sugar and spice and all things nice"?

   little girls ✓

8. What sweets are sometimes toasted on an open fire?

   marshmallows ✓

9. What sweet substance is made from nectar?

   Honey ✓

10. A ballerina might learn the Dance of the Sugar Plum... what?

    Fairy ✓

9/10

Picture Quiz . . . Flower Power

All these flowers begin with P. Can you name them?

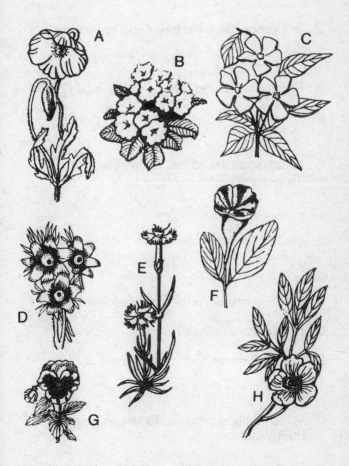

PERIWINKLE   PASSION FLOWER   POPPY
PETUNIA   PRIMROSE   PANSY   PINK   PEONY

General Quiz . . .

1. Which is larger, a violin or a viola?

   ViOLA ✓

2. In *Grange Hill*, what is Stebson's nickname?

   GRipper ✓

3. People who live in glass houses shouldn't do — what?

   throw stones. ✓

4. Which sport would you usually watch at Twickenham?

   Rugby Cricket ✓

5. In the old song, who lived on the River Dee?

   ? Jolly Miller ✗

6. In which country is the Costa del Sol? *Spain* ✓

7. How old is a centenarian? *100 yrs* ✓

8. From what animal does gammon come?

   Pig ✓

9. Which Biblical baby was hidden among the bulrushes?

   9/10

   Moses ✓

10. What does D.I.Y stand for? *Do it YERSELL* ✓

11. What drink is sometimes called "char"?

    Tea ✓

12. Which direction is opposite to North-East?

    South West ✓

13. What is another name for a tepee? ? Wigwam ✗

14. How many pence are there in five pounds? ......

    500 ✓

15. In which Dickens story does the character Pip
    appear?

    ? Great Expectations ✗

16. What common substance is made from latex?

    Foam Rubber ✓

17. Which Australian lady singer starred in the film
    Grease?

    ? O- Newtan John ✗

18. What might be short crust, flaky, puff or choux?

    Pastry ✓

19. Which American state is the home of the hula
    dance? ?

    Hawaii ✗

20. In olden times, what did schoolchildren write on?

    Slates ✓

6/10

Picture Quiz . . .

Can you name these types of aircraft?

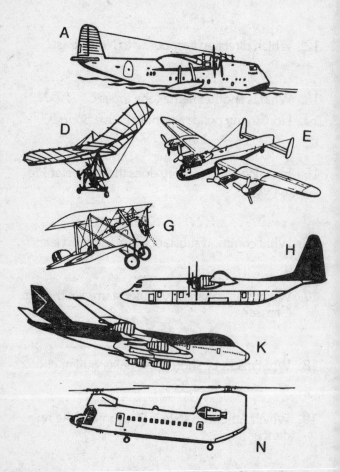

MICROLIGHT SOPWITH CAMEL CONCORDE
SPITFIRE SUNDERLAND FLYING BOAT
CHINOOK PIPER AZTEC

... High Flyers

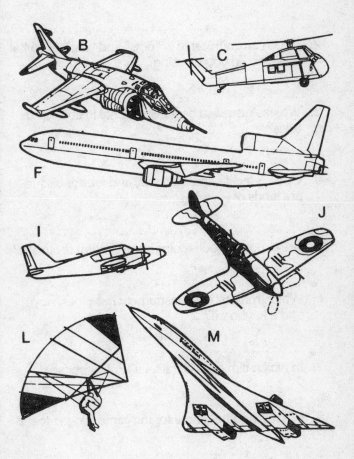

HERCULES HARRIER LANCASTER WESSEX
HANG GLIDER TRISTAR BOEING 747

General Quiz . . .

1. Who wrote the "Lone Pine" adventures?

   . . . .

2. If you communicated in "dots" and "dashes", what code would you be using?

   . . . . *Morse code* . . . .

3. Which Australian bear lives mainly in eucalyptus trees?

   . . . . *Koala* . . . .

4. Cock-a-leekie, mulligatawny and lobster bisque are kinds of . . . what?

   . . . . *Soup* . . . .

5. Are exported goods going into a country or out of it?

   . . . . *out* . . . .

6. Which musical wind instrument has pipes, stops and a keyboard?

   . . . .

7. In which film does Caractacus Potts appear?

   . . . .

8. What is another name for the game "tic-tac-toe"?

   . . . .

9. Nicholas II was the last Tsar of . . . where? . . . . . .

   . . . . *Russia* . . . .

10. What is the square root of 9? . . . *3* . . . .

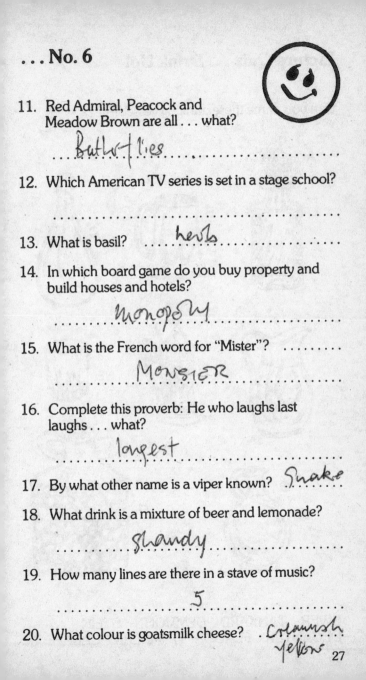

11. Red Admiral, Peacock and Meadow Brown are all . . . what?

    Butterflies

12. Which American TV series is set in a stage school?

13. What is basil?   herb

14. In which board game do you buy property and build houses and hotels?

    monopoly

15. What is the French word for "Mister"?

    MONSIER

16. Complete this proverb: He who laughs last laughs . . . what?

    longest

17. By what other name is a viper known?   Snake

18. What drink is a mixture of beer and lemonade?

    shandy

19. How many lines are there in a stave of music?

    5

20. What colour is goatsmilk cheese?   Colourish yellow

27

Picture Quiz ... Drink Up!

Can you name these drinking vessels?

Handwritten annotations on image:
- A — Decanter ✓
- B — Tankard ✓
- C — Carafe ✓
- D — Ewer, 5/8 ✓
- E — Demijohn (crossed out), Stein ✗
- F — Tumbler ✓
- G — Stein, Flagon
- H — Demijohn, Flagon ✓

EWER TANKARD DEMIJOHN STEIN ✓
DECANTER FLAGON TUMBLER CARAFE

Sound Effects

1. A whippoorwill is named after the noise it makes. What is it?

....

2. What word describes something that can travel faster than the speed of sound?

....

3. Which of these voices is the lowest — baritone, tenor, bass or alto?

....

4. What device was used for sounding the "All Clear" after a wartime bombing raid?

....

5. What does the musical instruction *forte* mean?

....

6. Which cereal is said to go "snap, crackle and pop"?

....

7. What is the swinging weight inside a bell called?

....

8. What noise can be known as "sawing wood"?

....

9. Which type of animal makes a baying noise?

....

10. What percussion instruments do Spanish dancers use?

....

29

General Quiz...

1. To which famous pop star was Yoko Ono married?

   John Lennon ✓

2. What are Grasmere, Erie, Como and Titicaca?

   Lakes ✓

3. Which metal does a clinical thermometer contain?

   mercury ✓

4. What does the Spanish word *toro* mean?

   ? Bull ✗

5. Who is the Patron of the Riding for the Disabled Association?

   Princess Anne ✓

6. In the book by Raymond Briggs, who is Fungus?

   ? Bogeyman ✗

7. Which meat is sometimes served as an "escalope"?

   Veal ✓

8. Which T.V. and film puppet characters were created by Jim Henson?

   the Muppets ✓

9. How many players are needed for a game of solitaire?

   One ✓

8/10

10. What are mace, coriander and cinnamon?

    Spices & Herbs ✓

11. Where does Paddington Bear's
    Aunt Lucy live?

    Peru ✓

12. Unleavened bread is bread made without . . .
    which ingredient?

    yeast ✓

13. What can a chameleon do that most other lizards
    can't?

    ? change colour ✗

14. In which state of the U.S.A. is Miami? Florida ✓

15. A man named Polo spent many years exploring
    China. What was his first name?

    Marco ✓

16. What is a baby swan called? . . . Cygnet ✓

17. Heathrow, Fiumicino and Orly are all . . . what?

    Airports ✓

18. With what are the names Axminster and Wilton
    connected?

    Carpets ✓

19. In Greek mythology, who killed the monster
    Medusa?

8/10   ✗ Perseus ?

20. Who was Kenneth More? . . . Actor ✓

Book Quiz

In which book can you read about

1. A rabbit who hides in an old man's garden?

. . . .

2. Lilliputians, Houyhnhnms and Yahoos? . . . .

. . . .

3. An old miser who hates Christmas? . . . .

4. Four American girls who called their mother "Marmee"?

. . . .

5. A little chimney-sweep who falls into a river?

. . . .

6. A nanny whose umbrella has a parrot's head handle?

. . . .

7. An evil Count who changes into a bat? . . . .

. . . .

8. Pauline, Petrova and Posy, who are taught to dance?

. . . .

9. A boy who finds a lucky ticket in a bar of chocolate?

. . . .

10. Peter, Susan, Edmund and Lucy in the land of Narnia?

. . . .

Picture Quiz . . . Find Your Feet

Name the footwear.

A trainers

B Brogues

C mules

D flip flops

E

F Clogs / galoshes

G Moccasins

TRAINERS   CLOGS   GALOSHES   MULES
BROGUES   FLIP-FLOPS   MOCCASINS

General Quiz . . .

1. In which sport might you use a Number 4 iron?

   golf

2. Where were the Prince and Princess of Wales married?

   St Pauls

3. What does S.R.N. stand for? *State Reg. Nurse*

4. Powdered tobacco which is sniffed up the nose — what is it called?

   Snuff

5. A drink and a Book of Records both have the same name. What is it?

6. In which famous book does the *Hispaniola* set sail?

7. A marsupial is an animal with a . . . what?

8. What does a choreographer create?

9. How many games are played in a decathlon event?

10. What flowers did Wordsworth see "dancing in the breeze"?

    daffodills

11. In which London park are the
    Serpentine and Rotten Row?

    .... St. James ....

12. A yeoman of the Tower of London is better known
    as a . . . what?

    .... Bee feater ....

13. How many consonants are there? ....21....

14. What is a John Dory? ....

15. On the fifth day of Christmas what did "my true
    love give to me"?

    ....

16. In the T.V. series *Dallas*, what does the "J.R." of
    "J.R. Ewing" stand for?

    ....

17. What is the name of Australia's national airline?

    ....

18. What name is given to the long rope carried by a
    cowboy?

    .... Lasoo ....

19. Where does an archer carry his arrows? ....

    ....

20. What kind of cooking is done in a wok? ....

    .... Chinese ....

Picture Quiz . . .

Which implement is which?

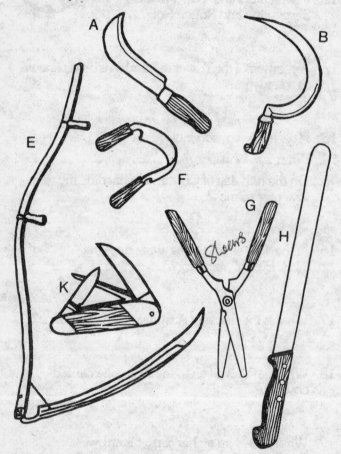

CHISEL   SCYTHE   JACK KNIFE   BILLHOOK
AXE   BREAD KNIFE   ADZE   MACHETE

...Look Sharp!

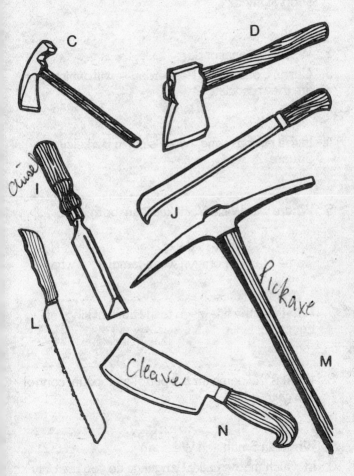

C

D

I Chisel

J

L

Pickaxe

M

Cleaver

N

DRAWSHAVE SICKLE SHEARS PICKAXE
CLEAVER HAM KNIFE

General Quiz . . .

1. Which cartoon character is small and bald and very short-sighted?

   . . . .

2. What is an anaconda? . . . .

3. Curry, Cousins and Pepperday—with which sport are they associated?

   . . . .

4. In the famous song, what "sang in Berkeley Square"?

   . . . .

5. Where was William Shakespeare born? . . . .

   . . . .

6. Dame Margot Fonteyn was a famous . . . what?

   . . . .

7. What was the title given to the ancient kings of Egypt?

   . . . .

8. What is the name for the petrol-air mixture control in a car?

   . . . .

9. What is a Smith and Wesson? . . . .

10. In which mathematical language do you use only noughts and ones?

   . . . .

11. What is another name for a bison?

....

12. What does W.P.C. stand for? ....

13. Where, on a uniform, are epaulettes worn?

....

14. In the books by Frank Muir, what kind of dog is What-A-Mess?

....

15. What type of food are macaroni, tagliatelle, lasagne and cannelloni?

....

16. In which T.V. programme does the presenter have a tea set in the arm of his chair?

....

17. How many sides has a 50p piece? ....

18. What is the Great Barrier Reef made of?

....

19. Which famous London concert hall was named after Queen Victoria's husband?

....

20. Where is the "Sea of Tranquillity"? ....

Picture Quiz . . . Panto Time

In which pantomimes would you see these?

RED RIDING HOOD   ALI BABA   ALADDIN
DICK WHITTINGTON   SLEEPING BEAUTY
CINDERELLA

Great Names

Can you identify these famous people?

1. A viscount called Horatio who died in the Battle of Trafalgar.

. . . .

2. An American singer whose films included *Jailhouse Rock* and *King Creole*?

. . . .

3. A queen of Egypt who killed herself with an asp.

. . . .

4. He starred in many Westerns and was known as "The Duke".

. . . .

5. The dancer who wanted John the Baptist's head.

. . . .

6. The German dictator who led Germany during the Second World War.

. . . .

7. The English king who gave up the throne for love.

. . . .

8. An English explorer who led an expedition to the South Pole in 1912.

. . . .

9. The fourth of Henry VIII's wives; she was called "The Flanders Mare".

. . . .

10. A 19th century American writer famous for his horrific "Tales of Mystery and Imagination".

. . . .

General Quiz . . .

1. What nationality was the boy-king Tutankhamun?

    . . . .

2. Parkhurst, Holloway, Wormwood Scrubs and Pentonville are all . . . what?

    . . . .

3. What is the name for a dramatic performance without words?

    . . . .

4. Where might you see isotherms and isobars?

    . . . .

5. What is an "s.a.e."? . . . .

6. Where would you find a space bar, a shift key and a carriage return lever?

    . . . .

7. What is Dennis the Menace's dog called?

    . . . .

8. What is a prune? . . . .

9. Which sign of the zodiac features a goat?

    . . . .

10. Who introduced tobacco and potatoes to England?

    . . . .

11. How many years are there in three score years and ten?

....

12. In which sport might you use a foil? ....

13. Do you eat hors d'oeuvres at the beginning or end of a meal?

....

14. What is a spinnaker? ....

15. In ancient times, where were the famous "Hanging Gardens"?

....

16. Parts of Britain were invaded by the Norsemen. By what name do we usually call them?

....

17. Who writes the *Mr. Men* books? ....

18. Which insect spreads malaria? ....

19. A leveret is a baby ... what? ....

20. In which city would you find Princes Street, Arthur's Seat and Holyrood Palace?

....

Ball Games

1. How many players are needed for a game of squash?

....

2. Which American game is similar to rounders?

....

3. What type of stick is used for both polo and croquet?

....

4. At which sport does Rachel Heyhoe Flint excel?

....

5. In volleyball, is the ball kicked, handled or hit with a bat?

....

6. Steve Davis and Alex "Hurricane" Higgins — what is their game?

....

7. In which sport do you carry a stick with a "cradle" at the end?

....

8. Which football team is known as Spurs?

....

9. What is a golfer's club-carrying attendant called?

....

10. In which sport might you "convert a try"?

....

Picture Quiz . . . Trademarks

Which well-known names are associated with these objects?

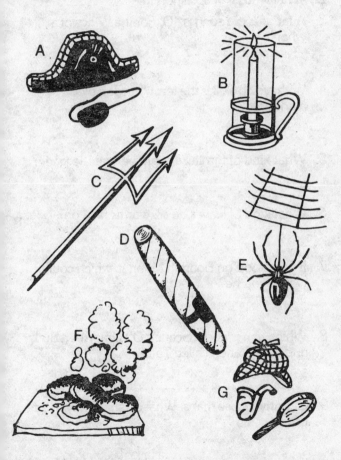

ROBERT THE BRUCE   FLORENCE NIGHTINGALE
SHERLOCK HOLMES   CHURCHILL   NELSON
KING ALFRED   NEPTUNE

General Quiz . . .

1. What is a sheepshank? . . . .
2. What word is "etc." short for? . . . .
3. A famous old song is "O, For the Wings of a . . . " what?

   . . . .
4. With which skill is the term "cordon bleu" associated?

   . . . .
5. What kind of furniture might be "gate-legged"?

   . . . .
6. What kind of leaves do silkworms feed on? . . . . .

   . . . .
7. If you stood on Bodmin Moor, in which county would you be?

   . . . .
8. Which film is about Scarlett O'Hara, Rhett Butler and a plantation called Tara?

   . . . .
9. Car drivers use maps. What do ships' navigators use?

   . . . .
10. In cockney rhyming slang, what is a titfer? . . . . . .

    . . . .

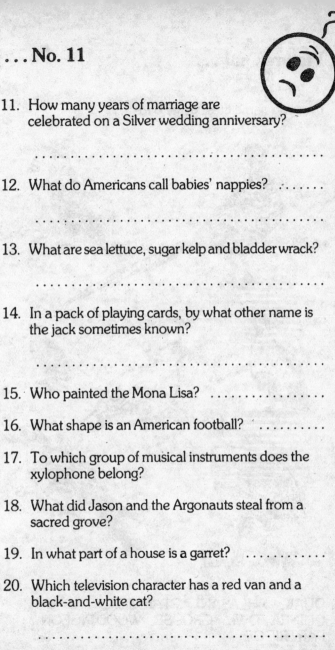

...No. 11

11. How many years of marriage are celebrated on a Silver wedding anniversary?

. . . .

12. What do Americans call babies' nappies? . . . .

. . . .

13. What are sea lettuce, sugar kelp and bladder wrack?

. . . .

14. In a pack of playing cards, by what other name is the jack sometimes known?

. . . .

15. Who painted the Mona Lisa? . . . .

16. What shape is an American football? . . . .

17. To which group of musical instruments does the xylophone belong?

18. What did Jason and the Argonauts steal from a sacred grove?

19. In what part of a house is a garret? . . . .

20. Which television character has a red van and a black-and-white cat?

. . . .

Picture Quiz . . .

Can you name these game birds . . .

QUAIL   PHEASANT   PTARMIGAN
GUINEA FOWL   GROUSE   WOOD PIGEON
PARTRIDGE

... All Birds

... and these sea birds?

STORMY PETREL ALBATROSS PUFFIN
CORMORANT PELICAN GANNET
HERRING GULL

49

General Quiz . . .

1. What are winkle-pickers? ... *Shoes - pointed toe*

2. The system of reading and writing for the blind consisting of raised dots is called . . . what?

   Braille

3. Which city has football clubs called Wednesday and United?

   Sheffield

4. Where, in London, is the Round Pond? ....

5. What is a Jewish place of worship called?

6. In what kind of building can you find a nave?

7. In Greek legend, who was the wife of Zeus?

8. Which world leader is protected by the Swiss Guard?

9. What breed of dog has a name that means "badger hound"?

10. How many dimes are there in a U.S. dollar?

11. Which country is associated with the song "Land of my Fathers"?

....

12. What are Kilimanjaro, Skiddaw, McKinley and the Matterhorn?

....

13. Which two colours are associated with the Wars of the Roses?

....

14. Mozart wrote an opera called "The Marriage of . . ." who?

....

15. What is the dish consisting of batter and sausages called?

....

16. Harrison Ford starred in a film called *Raiders of the Lost* . . . what?

....

17. What is the German for "No"? ....

18. How long did Lady Jane Grey reign as queen — nine days, nine months or nine years?

....

19. What does a philatelist collect? ....

20. Which Indian city became famous for its Black Hole?

....

Picture Quiz ... Little Beasts

They may be small, but they're very fierce.
Can you name them?

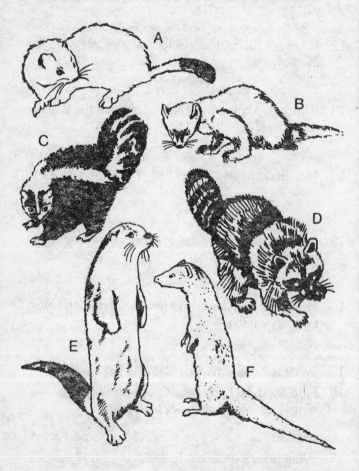

ERMINE OTTER MARTEN MONGOOSE
SKUNK RACCOON

Here and There

1. Which country uses yens as currency?

....

2. Which English county is famous for its hot pot?

....

3. Where, in the song, did Molly Malone live?

....

4. In which famous city will you find Broadway, Times Square and 42nd Street?

....

5. T.E. Lawrence, the soldier and writer, became known as Lawrence of . . . where?

....

6. In which country might you be wished *"God morgon!"*?

....

7. Where do Maoris come from? ....

8. Palm trees, calypsos, rum punch and reggae — you'll find them all in the West . . . what?

....

9. What was the name of the legendary city of King Arthur?

....

10. In which continent would you find people of the Ojibwa and Tutsi tribes?

....

General Quiz . . .

1. Who was Benjamin Britten? . . . .

2. What is the underground train system in Paris called?

   . . . .

3. If you suffered from vertigo, would you feel itchy, tearful, hot or dizzy?

   . . . .

4. Members of The Society of Friends are better known as . . . what?

   . . . .

5. Which large birds are renowned for building their nests on roof-tops?

   . . . .

6. What does the chemical H_2O stand for? . . . .

   . . . .

7. Who wrote the music for *Evita*, *Jesus Christ Superstar* and *Cats*?

   . . . .

8. In which city is the Parthenon? . . . .

9. What is Harry Webb's stage name? . . . .

10. Where can you see the Crown Jewels? . . . .

   . . . .

11. Does a loofah grow above or below the ground, or in the sea?

    ....

12. Which American president was a one-time peanut farmer?

    ....

13. What does a hod-carrier carry in his hod?

    ....

14. What are the Gobi, the Kara-Kum, the Mohave and the Kalahari?

    ....

15. Which liner hit an iceberg and sank on its maiden voyage?

    ....

16. What is a baby kangaroo called? ....

17. How many metres are there in a kilometre?

    ....

18. What is Spartak? ....

19. What item of footwear is named after a famous duke?

    ....

20. What is a Dandie Dinmont? ....

Stars and Planets

1. Which planet is nearest to Earth?

   . . . .

2. What lies at the centre of the Solar System?

   . . . .

3. What animal is the star constellation Ursa Major supposed to look like?

   . . . .

4. Who are, or were, Yuri Gagarin and John Glenn?

   . . . .

5. Which planet has the name of a famous cartoon dog?

   . . . .

6. Earth has just one satellite. What is it called?

   . . . .

7. Are the particles which make up Saturn's rings very hot or very cold?

   . . . .

8. Who was the villain in the film *Star Wars*?

   . . . .

9. What name is given to the scientific study of stars and planets?

   . . . .

10. Which planet is sometimes known as the evening star?

    . . . .

Picture Quiz . . . Roots

Which is which?

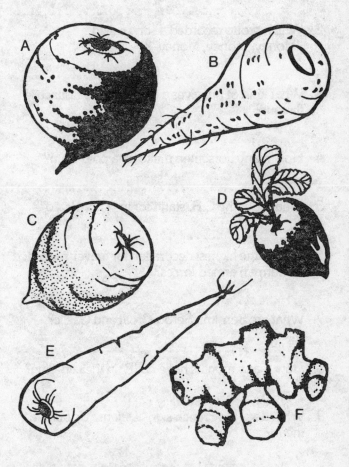

TURNIP RADISH GINGER PARSNIP
BEETROOT CARROT

General Quiz . . .

1. What kind of creature is a roadrunner? . . . .
. . . .

2. Which group recorded a song called "Money, Money, Money"?
. . . .

3. What kind of nut gives a macaroon its distinctive flavour?
. . . .

4. How many horsemen make up a polo team?
. . . .

5. What does the C.B. stand for in "C.B. Radio"?
. . . .

6. What is the highest decoration for bravery awarded to German armed forces?
. . . .

7. What are Sanskrit, Serbo-Croat and Gaelic?
. . . .

8. How many months have no 'R' in their spelling?
. . . .

9. What does the French sign "*Defense de Fumée*" mean?
. . . .

10. A mischievous elf in Irish folklore is called a . . . what?
. . . .

11. What name is given to a violently spinning funnel-shaped cloud?

. . . .

12. From which animal is the fur called coney obtained?

. . . .

13. What was the "Flying Scotsman"? . . . .

14. Rollmops — do you hit them, eat them, listen to them or clean with them?

. . . .

15. What sporting activity is associated with Cowes?

. . . .

16. In Edward Lear's poem, who "had no toes"?

. . . .

17. What do criminals mean by "porridge"?

. . . .

18. What is the first letter of the Greek alphabet?

. . . .

19. What is the book called in which a pilot records his flights?

. . . .

20. In the Bible, who was the youngest of Jacob's twelve sons?

. . . .

Picture Quiz . . . .

Do you know what each of these is called?

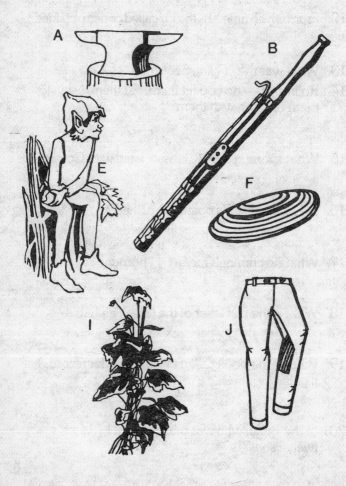

A

B

E

F

I

J

. . . What Is It?

The first begins with A, the second with B, and so on.

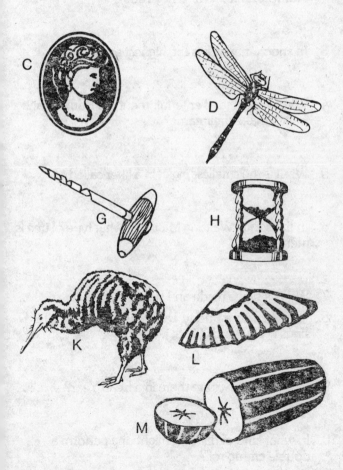

General Quiz . . .

1. What is a quince? . . . .
2. Which children's T.V. programme features Humpty, Jemima and Big Ted?

   . . . .

3. In snooker, which is the highest scoring ball?

   . . . .

4. With what kind of entertainment did Barnum and Bailey make their name?

   . . . .

5. What is the smallest piglet in a litter called?

   . . . .

6. In the song "Waltzing Matilda", what type of tree is mentioned?

   . . . .

7. What is silage made and stored in? . . . .
8. "I Tort I Taw a Puddy Tat" — which cartoon bird sings these words?

   . . . .

9. How many days are there in a Leap Year? . . . . . .

   . . . .

10. In what kind of dancing might one perform a double cramp roll?

    . . . .

11. What sort of person would you call "Your Excellency"?

. . . .

12. What does the French expression *mal de mer* mean?

. . . .

13. At which race meeting do the Royal Family ride up the course in open carriages?

. . . .

14. How were Wilbur and Orville Wright, aircraft pioneers, related to each other?

. . . .

15. What is the capital of the Falkland Islands?

. . . .

16. Which part of the liquorice plant is used to make sweets?

. . . .

17. The messenger of the Gods was called Mercury by the Romans. What name did the Greeks use?

. . . .

18. With which sport are the terms Chinaman, nightwatchman and gully associated?

. . . .

19. What is another name for a string puppet?

. . . .

20. What is the first book of the Old Testament called?

. . . .

Picture Quiz . . . Robes

Which garment is which?

KIMONO PONCHO SARI KAFTAN SARONG
JELLABAH

Eating Out

1. In what kind of restaurant would you be offered poppadoms?

....

2. What type of service will you find in a cafeteria?

....

3. If you had a "quarter-pounder", what would you be eating?

....

4. In a smart restaurant, you choose the food from the menu and the drink from the ... what?

....

5. What is often used instead of salt in a Chinese restaurant?

....

6. How is paté usually eaten? ....

7. What name is given to a cook in a restaurant?

....

8. What are French fries? ....

9. From which country did pizza originally come?

....

10. Is a bistro a large or a small restaurant? ....

....

General Quiz . . .

1. What is a rabbit's tail called? . . . .

2. Who was the great-great-grandmother of Queen Elizabeth II?

   . . . .

3. What type of musical instrument is a Stradivarius?

   . . . .

4. On which day of the week is Mothers' Day?

   . . . .

5. With which part of the body is an oculist concerned?

   . . . .

6. What articles of clothing are called drainpipes?

   . . . .

7. Cantaloupe, ogen and honeydew are all types of . . . what?

   . . . .

8. What nationality was King Canute? . . . .

9. Who was Rudolph Valentino? . . . .

10. What does a cooper make? . . . .

11. How many players are there in a British lacrosse team?

....

12. With what do you associate floppy discs, V.D.U.s and print-outs?

....

13. What can be stacked, Cuban, stiletto or wedge?

....

14. In which sport might you take on a southpaw?

....

15. What is a jacaranda? ....

16. With what profession is the name Barrymore connected?

....

17. Aircraft and ships measure their speed in . . . what?

....

18. In Greek mythology, what was Hercules renowned for?

....

19. What name is given to a jug made in the form of a man in a three-cornered hat?

....

20. What colour does litmus paper turn when dipped in acid?

....

Laughing Matters

1. Which comedian plays the piano badly on purpose?

   . . . .

2. Who took his stage name from an English seaside resort?

   . . . .

3. Who pulls at his braces — Cannon or Ball?

   . . . .

4. Whose names mean "small and big"? . . . .

   . . . .

5. Which impersonator has a T.V. show called "In Persons"?

   . . . .

6. Which comic sometimes dresses as a boy scout?

   . . . .

7. Dr. Evadne Hinge's partner is Dame Hilda . . . what?

   . . . .

8. What is Rod Hull's bird puppet called? . . . .

   . . . .

9. Graeme Garden, Tim Brooke-Taylor and Bill Oddie — what do they call themselves?

   . . . .

10. Whose catchphrase is "Just like that?" . . . .

   . . . .

Picture Quiz . . . All Lit Up

Which is which?

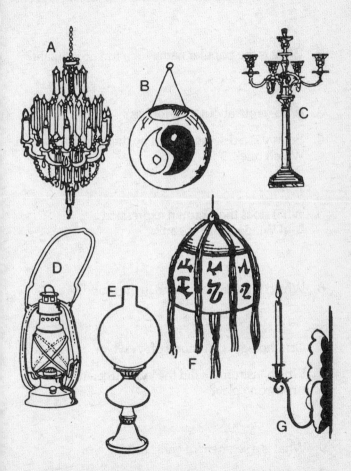

JAPANESE LANTERN   CANDELABRA   OIL LAMP
CHANDELIER   CHINESE LANTERN   SCONCE
HURRICANE LANTERN

General Quiz . . .

1. Which crop is attacked by the boll weevil? . . . . . .

. . . .

2. What is the popular name for a turf accountant?

. . . .

3. Who wrote about the Hobbits? . . . .

4. Scurvy is a disease caused by the lack of a vitamin. Which one?

. . . .

5. What does the German expression "auf Wiedersehn" mean?

. . . .

6. Which is the largest island in the world? . . . .

. . . .

7. Ornithology is the study of . . . what? . . . .

8. Which instrument did the jazz musician Louis Armstrong play?

. . . .

9. What is a segment of garlic called? . . . .

10. For which activity might you use a pair of number nines and a row counter?

. . . .

11. What is, or was, a peruke? . . . .

12. In which game can you be castled?

. . . .

13. Which kind of Siamese cat has a brown mask, paws and tail and a cream body?

. . . .

14. Which darts champion is known as the "Crafty Cockney"?

. . . .

15. What is the name of the pub in *Coronation Street*?

. . . .

16. In which famous, high-kicking dance do girls in frilly petticoats do the splits?

. . . .

17. When is St. Valentine's Day? . . . .

18. Which English king did the Roundheads oppose?

. . . .

19. Lucky at cards, unlucky in . . . what? . . . .

20. Which poem tells of a town over-run by rats?

. . . .

Picture Quiz . . .

The first begins with N, the second with O, and so on.

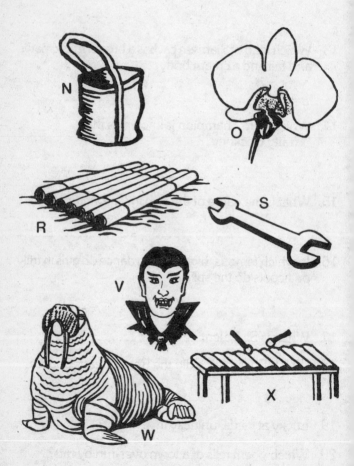

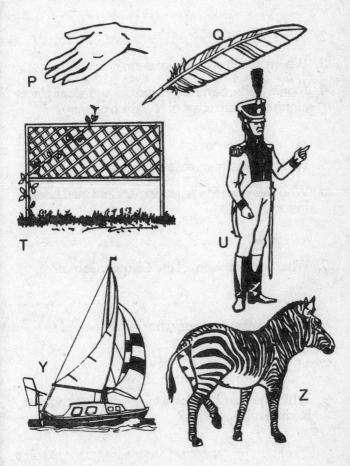

P

Q

T

U

Y

Z

General Quiz ...

1. In the T.V. series *Nanny*, who played the title role?

. . . .

2. What is the N.S.B.? . . . .

3. Where would you use secateurs? . . . .

4. Monte Carlo, San Tropez and Cannes are all places along the south coast of . . . which country?

. . . .

5. What is a wet burn called? . . . .

6. Who was born Margaret Roberts and made British history?

. . . .

7. What is the emblem of the Olympic Games?

. . . .

8. In Longfellow's poem, who was the wife of Hiawatha?

. . . .

9. Which queen of the Iceni tribe led a revolt against Roman rule in Britain?

. . . .

10. In which type of sport might you use a Fosbury Flop?

. . . .

11. How many crosses make up the Union flag?

   . . . .

12. By what name was the Indian leader Mohandas Karamchand Gandhi better known?

   . . . .

13. In 1858, John Hanning Speke discovered the source of . . . which river?

   . . . .

14. Who went to sea with "silver buckles at his knee"?

   . . . .

15. What is another name for Devonshire cream?

   . . . .

16. In which year was Queen Elizabeth II crowned? Was it 1952, 1953, or 1955?

   . . . .

17. What type of animal was Guy, of London Zoo?

   . . . .

18. After whom is the month of July named? . . . .

   . . . .

19. What does a tanner produce? . . . .

20. In which books can you find Violet Elizabeth Bott?

   . . . .

75

Picture Quiz . . . Sounds of the Past

Can you name these musical instruments?

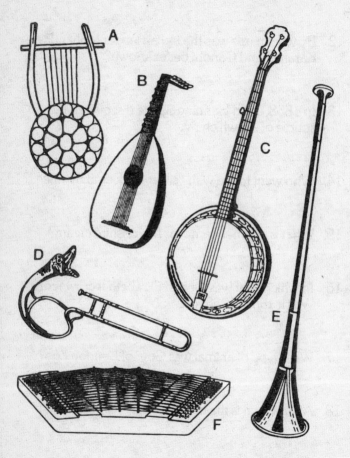

BANJO DULCIMER LYRE SACKBUT
POST HORN LUTE

Horses and Ponies

1. Shire, Shetland, Clydesdale, Suffolk Punch —
   which is the odd one out?

   . . . .

2. Where on a horse would you find a chestnut?

   . . . .

3. What was the famous winged horse of Greek
   legend called?

   . . . .

4. In what way was George Stubbs connected with
   horses?

   . . . .

5. What is a young male horse called? . . . .

6. What is, or was, an ostler? . . . .

7. Anna Sewell wrote a famous book about a horse.
   What's the title?

   . . . .

8. A golden-haired horse with a silvery mane and tail
   — what is it called?

   . . . .

9. In which race do horses jump Bechers Brook?

   . . . .

10. A cross between a male donkey and a female horse
    is called a . . . what?

    . . . .

General Quiz . . .

1. Who or what was Moby Dick? . . . .

2. On which island can you find a village called Llanfairpwllgwyngyllgogerychwyrndro-bwllllantysiliogogogoch?

. . . .

3. Mary Tudor was the daughter of Henry VIII. Who was her mother?

. . . .

4. If a person is a hypochondriac, he imagines that he is . . . what?

. . . .

5. Who wrote *The Time Machine*? . . . .

6. What kind of movement is a pirouette? . . . .

. . . .

7. How many spots are there on a dice? . . . .

8. Which canal cuts through Central America?

. . . .

9. What kind of animal might be a Southdown, Cheviot or Romney Marsh?

. . . .

10. In the book *Tom Sawyer*, what is the name of Tom's aunt?

. . . .

11. If you suffered from agoraphobia, what would you be afraid of?

   . . . .

12. If you were talking to a bishop, what should you call him?

   . . . .

13. Which country fought England with a fleet of ships called the Armada?

   . . . .

14. What is the name of the submarine in *20,000 Leagues Under the Sea*?

   . . . .

15. Paddington, Waterloo and Victoria are all London . . . what?

   . . . .

16. The Wrekin is in Shropshire. What is it? . . . .

   . . . .

17. What is the word "pram" short for? . . . .

18. Claridges, Raffles, the Waldorf-Astoria and the George V are all famous . . . what?

   . . . .

19. Whose Piano Concerto No. 5 was nicknamed "The Emperor"?

   . . . .

20. With which sport do you connect the names Boomerang, Sportsman, Marius and Ryan's Son?

   . . . .

Threesomes

What do these names have in common?

1. Benjamin Disraeli, David Lloyd George, James Callaghan.

. . . .

2. Tracey Austin, John McEnroe, Vitas Gerulaitis.

. . . .

3. Discovery, Russet, Cox's Orange Pippin.

. . . .

4. Rosemary Sutcliff, Alan Garner, Leon Garfield.

. . . .

5. Ann Boleyn, Marie Antoinette, Sir Thomas More.

. . . .

6. Sebastian Coe, Sonia Lannerman, Steve Ovett.

. . . .

7. Derwent, Severn, Medway.

. . . .

8. Canaletto, Toulouse Lautrec, El Greco.

. . . .

9. Spectrum, Pet, Apple.

. . . .

10. Shakin' Stevens, Adam Ant, Elton John.

. . . .

Quick Quiz . . . Teatime

Can you name these cakes?

A

B

C

D

E

F

DOUGHNUT   SWISS ROLL   ECCLES CAKE
ECLAIR   VICTORIA SPONGE   BATTENBURG

General Quiz . . .

1. Where do Monegasques come from? . . . .

. . . .

2. What name is given to an otter's den? . . . .

. . . .

3. Which traditional delicacy is made of offal, oatmeal and suet, boiled in a sheep's stomach?

. . . .

4. What part of the body does hepatitis affect?

. . . .

5. For which type of art form is Henry Moore famous?

. . . .

6. What is an ugli? . . . .

7. Which ancient people worshipped cats?

. . . .

8. Cirrus, stratus, nimbus and cumulus are all . . . what?

. . . .

9. In 1976 James Hunt became a world champion. At which sport?

. . . .

10. What is the meaning of the Prince of Wales's motto *Ich Dien*?

. . . .

11. In which book does a gull named Kehaar help some rabbits?

....

12. What do the initials C.N.D. stand for? ....

....

13. Which science fiction author introduced a T.V. series called *Mysterious Worlds*?

....

14. How many "ha'pennies" are used in a game of shove ha'penny?

....

15. What are Roedean, Wycombe Abbey, Heathfield and Benenden?

....

16. Which volcano erupted in AD 79, smothering Pompeii in ash and lava?

....

17. Who built Hampton Court Palace? ....

18. Which is the higher rank — Major-General or Lieutenant-General?

....

19. If someone committed matricide, whom would he have killed?

....

20. Which saint's day is on April 23rd? ....

Picture Quiz ...

Can you identify these chairs and sofas?

BASKET LADDERBACK THRONE PORTER'S
WING CHAISE LONGUE LOVE SEAT SETTEE

... Take a Seat

WINDSOR   CHIPPENDALE   CORNER
BUTTONBACK

General Quiz ...

1. Who are Shiva, Vishnu and Brahma? . . . .
   . . . .

2. What is a coiffure? . . . .

3. In which type of fabric printing are designs applied
   in wax?
   . . . .

4. Who was captain of *The Endeavour*? . . . .
   . . . .

5. When was the first England v. Australia Test
   Match? Was it 1877, 1901 or 1926?
   . . . .

6. Of which country is Szechuan a province?
   . . . .

7. According to legend, Walpurgis Night is celebrated
   by . . . who or what?
   . . . .

8. By what name is the fictional character Sir Percy
   Blakeney better known?
   . . . .

9. Who composed "The Four Seasons"? . . . .

10. In the Royal Navy, what is a C.P.O.? . . . .
    . . . .

11. Beam, arch, suspension and cantilever are the four basic types of ... what?

....

12. Who is the questionmaster on T.V.'s *Mastermind*?

....

13. In which sport might you follow a piste? ....

....

14. What is the emblem on the cap badge of the Welsh Guards?

....

15. Who wrote *Das Kapital*? ....

16. What is the word "cello" short for? ....

17. What might be described as crewel, packing, darning or larding?

....

18. The mazurka is a national dance of ... which country?

....

19. In Italy, if someone said to you: "*Felice compleanno!*" What day would it be?

....

20. What was the first name of President Brezhnev of the Soviet Union?

....

Picture Quiz . . . Creepy-Crawlies

Can you name them?

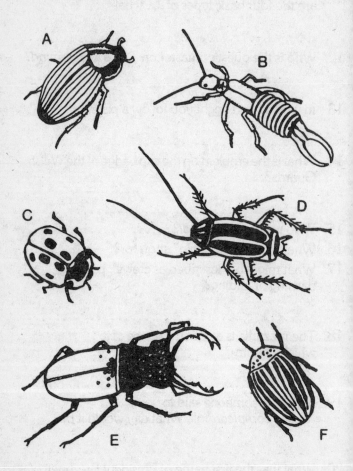

STAG BEETLE   LADYBIRD   COCKROACH
EARWIG   COLORADO BEETLE   JUNE BUG

Crime and Detection

1. Which famous detective had a friend called Watson?

   . . . .

2. London was once terrorized by Jack the . . . what?

   . . . .

3. Who likes lollipops and says "Who loves ya, baby?"

   . . . .

4. Which English writer was known as the "Queen of Crime"?

   . . . .

5. In which film did Inspector Clouseau first appear?

   . . . .

6. Who killed Cock Robin? . . . .

7. Bill Sikes murdered Nancy in a book by Charles Dickens. Which one?

   . . . .

8. In court, if a prisoner "takes the stand", where does he go?

   . . . .

9. Which city does the Metropolitan Police Force look after?

   . . . .

10. How did Brutus kill Julius Caesar? . . . .

General Quiz . . .

1. What does a starfish do when it loses an arm?

. . . .

2. Who is supposed to have made an important scientific discovery while in his bath?

. . . .

3. Which island forms a republic with Trinidad?

. . . .

4. If you were put in a pillory, would you have to stand, sit or lie down?

. . . .

5. At which racecourse is the Grand National run?

. . . .

6. The official country residence of the Prime Minister is called . . . what?

. . . .

7. In which sport do players compete for the Swaythling Cup?

. . . .

8. Which general was killed at the Battle of Little Bighorn?

. . . .

9. What is the title of a marquess's wife? . . . .

10. In which type of dancing might you perform an entrechat?

. . . .

11. What is a colobus? . . . .

12. How many pieces are there in a set of dominoes?

. . . .

13. The Leopard, the Sherman and the Chieftain are all types of . . . what?

. . . .

14. What do the letters O.H.M.S. stand for? . . . .

. . . .

15. Which number is represented by the Roman numeral CLXXIV?

. . . .

16. What do entomologists study? . . . .

17. Who wrote the poem *Paradise Lost*? . . . .

. . . .

18. What is an auctioneer's hammer called? . . . .

. . . .

19. Colour television pictures are produced from three colours: red, blue and . . . what?

. . . .

20. What kind of bone was once used for stiffening corsets?

. . . .

Sleepyheads

1. Who was "under a haystack, fast asleep"?

. . . .

2. Who, in a story by Washington Irving, fell asleep for 20 years?

. . . .

3. What name is given to a short rest during the heat of the noonday sun?

. . . .

4. Which Old Testament character had a dream about fat and lean cattle?

. . . .

5. "Sleep, my love, and peace attend thee . . ." What words come next in this old Welsh song?

. . . .

6. How many "winks" make a short sleep? . . . .

7. A bump across a road to slow down traffic is known as sleeping . . . what?

. . . .

8. What does Wee Willie Winkie wear as he runs through the town?

. . . .

9. Who wrote "A Midsummer Night's Dream"?

. . . .

10. Animals who sleep through the winter are said to . . . what?

. . . .

Picture Quiz . . . Marine Life

Can you name these animals of the sea?

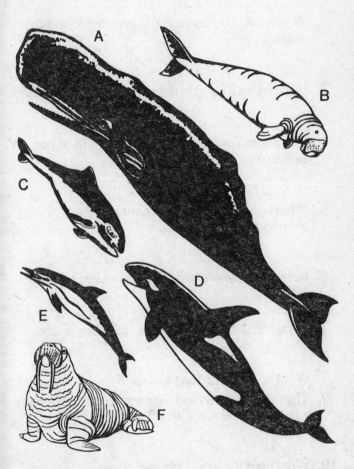

KILLER WHALE   DUGONG   PORPOISE
SPERM WHALE   DOLPHIN   WALRUS

General Quiz . . .

1. What type of creature is a pipistrelle? . . . .

. . . .

2. Which milk pudding is made from the root of the cassava plant?

. . . .

3. What name is given to the science of sound waves?

. . . .

4. The singer Toyah is also an actress. What is her surname?

. . . .

5. What is the more common name for the astronomical term "collapsar"?

. . . .

6. In the Bible, what was odd about Balaam's donkey?

. . . .

7. For which kind of shellfish is Dublin Bay famous?

. . . .

8. What is, or was, a "half-hunter"? . . . .

9. The art of knotting and weaving coarse thread into a pattern is called . . . what?

. . . .

10. What does the word "piscine" mean? . . . .

. . . .

11. Euclid is known as "The Father of . . ." which branch of mathematics?

. . . .

12. What is the sacred book of the Moslem faith called?

. . . .

13. Some vehicles have to pass the M.O.T. test. What do the letters stand for?

. . . .

14. What is the capital of Afghanistan? . . . .

15. The House of Commons is to Britain as Stormont is to . . . where?

. . . .

16. What is a "brass hat"? . . . .

17. Who was the last of the Norman kings? . . . .

. . . .

18. What type of injury can sometimes be described by the word "greenstick"?

. . . .

19. In "The Teddy Bears' Picnic", when do their mummies and daddies take them home?

. . . .

20. Who was Bob Hope's partner in the "Road" films?

. . . .

Picture Quiz . . .

Rulers of the world — which is which?

GRANDEE   TSAR   MANDARIN   MOGUL
SHOGUN   PHARAOH

RAJAH   KAISER   SHAH   SULTAN

General Quiz . . .

1. What are woofers and tweeters? . . . .

2. Of which planet is Io a satellite? . . . .

3. What nationality was Cleopatra? . . . .

4. Which Italian painter had a name which means "Little Dyer"?

   . . . .

5. The Harpies were mythical beasts. They were half bird, half . . . what?

   . . . .

6. What is the better-known title of the Primate of All England?

   . . . .

7. Who was the brother of Anne, Emily and Charlotte Brontë?

   . . . .

8. What shape is a "clay pigeon"? . . . .

9. In aeronautics, what does V.T.O.L. stand for?

   . . . .

10. What kind of creature is a bonito? . . . .

    . . . .

11. Which ancient structure runs from the Solway Firth to the mouth of the Tyne?

. . . .

12. A picture made by weaving coloured threads into a fixed warp is called a . . . what?

. . . .

13. Who was the first man to run a mile in four minutes?

. . . .

14. What are rising currents of warm air called?

. . . .

15. If you were lacrimose, what would you be doing?

. . . .

16. Which country was formerly called East Pakistan?

. . . .

17. What was the particular skill of Charles Blondin?

. . . .

18. "Arsenal v. West Ham United." What does the "v" stand for?

. . . .

19. What word describes someone who has alopecia?

. . . .

20. The U.S.A. has two main political parties, the Republicans and the . . . what?

. . . .

Famous Dogs

1. What breed of dog is the film star Lassie?

    . . . .

2. In which story do Dorothy and her dog Toto
    appear?

    . . . .

3. What is the name of the dog in *Peter Pan*?

    . . . .

4. Who is Charlie Brown's dog in the "Peanuts"
    cartoons?

    . . . .

5. Petra, Shep and Goldie — in which T.V.
    programme have they appeared?

    . . . .

6. Who owns the most famous corgis in the world?

    . . . .

7. What was the name of the *Magic Roundabout* dog?

    . . . .

8. In which T.V. series does Freeway appear?

    . . . .

9. A Pekingese and a mongrel starred in a famous
    Disney cartoon film. Which one?

    . . . .

10. Which dog is one of Enid Blyton's "Famous Five"?

    . . . .

Boats

1. What kind of bird travelled in a "pea-green boat"?

   . . . .

2. On which river is the Oxford and Cambridge Boat Race rowed?

   . . . .

3. What is a "water boatman"? . . . .

4. In *The Wind in the Willows* who loved "messing about in boats"?

   . . . .

5. What is a boater usually made from? . . . .

   . . . .

6. The letters R.N.L.I. stand for the Royal National . . . what?

   . . . .

7. Where would you expect to find a narrowboat?

   . . . .

8. Which public school has a special boating song?

   . . . .

9. On a rowing boat, what are held in place by the rowlocks?

   . . . .

10. Where in Italy can you ride in a gondola? . . . .

    . . . .

General Quiz . . .

1. Who wrote *The Secret Garden*? . . . .

2. Where do Orcadians live? . . . .

3. Who might use a Hairy Dog, Sweeny Todd, Woolly Worm or Missionary?

   . . . .

4. A brad is a kind of . . . what? . . . .

5. Which word describes someone who is equally expert with each hand?

   . . . .

6. Fortran and Cobol are both types of . . . which kind of language?

   . . . .

7. If you travel incognito you travel in . . . what?

   . . . .

8. Which number on a dart board lies between the numbers 1 and 5?

   . . . .

9. Who was the last Viceroy of India? . . . .

10. Of which group of Pacific islands is Suva the capital?

    . . . .

11. London's Marble Arch stands on an old gallows site. What was it called?

. . . .

12. Which sport was once known as Sphairistike?

. . . .

13. What nationality was the composer Franz Liszt?

. . . .

14. The Knesset is the name of the parliament of . . . which country?

. . . .

15. How does a costermonger display his wares?

. . . .

16. In which song are Tummel and Loch Rannoch and Lochaber mentioned?

. . . .

17. Who said: "Kinkering kongs their tatles tike"?

. . . .

18. Which American female singer has the same name as a town on the river Avon?

. . . .

19. In Dickens's *David Copperfield*, what was the occupation of Mr. Creakle?

. . . .

20. Which film actress was originally named Norma Jean Mortenson?

. . . .

Monsters

1. How many eyes has a Cyclops? . . . .

2. The Yeti is another name for . . . what?

    . . . .

3. Who created a monster in a book by Mary Shelley?

    . . . .

4. Which giant ape climbed up the Empire State
    Building?

    . . . .

5. What grew out of the Gorgons' heads?

    . . . .

6. Which monster was apparently seen by
    St. Columbia?

    . . . .

7. Who slew the monster Grendel? . . . .

8. What was a triceratops? . . . .

9. Who was the monster — Dr. Jekyll or Mr. Hyde?

    . . . .

10. The Minotaur was half man, half . . . what?

    . . . .

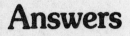

Answers

General Quiz No. 1
1. James Bond. 2. Three. 3. Man Friday. 4. Uncle. 5. Moon.
6. The elephant. 7. Spades. 8. Eggs. 9. The thistle. 10. Aunt
Sally. 11. A tall glass. 12. Mount Everest. 13. Wasp. 14. A lion.
15. Peter Piper. 16. *Alice in Wonderland*. 17. Little John.
18. A helicopter. 19. The cuckoo. 20. King Arthur.

Colours
1. Brown. 2. Blue. 3. Yellow. 4. Seven. 5. White. 6. Pink.
7. Orange. 8. Green. 9. Insects. 10. Black.

Picture Quiz — Say Cheese!
A. Brie. B. Stilton. C. Cheddar. D. Cottage. E. Gruyère.
F. Edam.

General Quiz No. 2
1. Grapes. 2. Ten. 3. The eyelashes. 4. Tail. 5. Charlie
Chaplin. 6. Beer. 7. Indian. 8. April 1st. 9. Chopsticks.
10. Please turn over. 11. Paris. 12. Beds. 13. Knights. 14. An
Atlas. 15. *E.T.* 16. John Brown's. 17. Christmas. 18. A vixen.
19. *Blue Peter*. 20. Banks.

Picture Quiz — Inside You
A. Deltoid. B. Biceps. C. Pectorals. D. Diaphragm.
E. Hamstring. F. Achilles Tendon. G. Mastoid. H. Clavicle.
I. Sternum. J. Femur. K. Patella. L. Fibula.

General Quiz No. 3
1. Dr. Who. 2. A pearl. 3. Australian. 4. Red. 5. A town crier.
6. Lamb. 7. Tony Hart. 8. Horses. 9. Two. 10. Barbara
Woodhouse. 11. Beatrix Potter. 12. The cobra. 13. A Punch
and Judy show. 14. Biggles. 15. Doc. 16. A wall.
17. On Wednesday. 18. Rink. 19. Holland. 20. Fables.

Picture Quiz — Sticks and Staffs
A. Shooting stick. B. Malacca cane. C. Crosier.
D. Thumbstick. E. Swagger stick. F. Pike staff.

Gold and Silver
1. King Midas. 2. The Lone Ranger. 3. Goldilocks. 4. Lining.
5. Soft. 6. A salver. 7. A goldsmith. 8. The silver birch. 9. A
goldfish. 10. Rolls-Royce.

General Quiz No. 4
1. A cat. 2. The flute. 3. Ten thousand. 4. Apples. 5. Ringo
Starr. 6. A turban. 7. The Borrowers. 8. An oasis. 9. The
Krankies. 10. Black Bess. 11. A windmill. 12. *Annie*. 13. Your
feet. 14. Touch. 15. Pancakes. 16. Freshwater. 17. An
unmarried man. 18. Norfolk. 19. Mounties. 20. Rice.

Sweet Things
1. Gingerbread. 2. Potato. 3. Biscuits. 4. Brazil. 5. Sixteen.
6. Meringue. 7. Little girls. 8. Marshmallow. 9. Honey.
10. Fairy.

Picture Quiz — Flower Power
A. Poppy. B. Primrose. C. Periwinkle. D. Passion Flower.
E. Pink. F. Petunia. G. Pansy. H. Peony.

Page 22/23

General Quiz No. 5
1. A viola. 2. Gripper. 3. Throw stones. 4. Rugby Union. 5. A jolly miller. 6. Spain. 7. 100 years. 8. A pig. 9. Moses. 10. Do It Yourself. 11. Tea. 12. South-West. 13. Wigwam. 14. Five hundred. 15. *Great Expectations*. 16. Rubber. 17. Olivia Newton-John. 18. Pastry. 19. Hawaii. 20. Slates.

Page 24/25

Picture Quiz — High Flyers
A. Sunderland Flying Boat. B. Harrier. C. Wessex.
D. Microlite. E. Lancaster. F. Tristar. G. Sopwith Camel.
H. Hercules. I. Piper Aztec. J. Spitfire. K. Boeing 747.
L. Hang glider. M. Concorde. N. Chinook.

Page 26/27

General Quiz No. 6
1. Malcolm Saville. 2. Morse. 3. The koala. 4. Soup. 5. Out. 6. The organ. 7. *Chitty Chitty Bang Bang*. 8. Noughts and crosses. 9. Russia. 10. Three. 11. Butterflies. 12. *Fame*. 13. A herb. 14. Monopoly. 15. *Monsieur*. 16. Longest. 17. Adder. 18. Shandy. 19. Five. 20. White.

Page 28

Picture Quiz — Drink Up!
A. Decanter. B. Tankard. C. Carafe. D. Ewer. E. Stein.
F. Tumbler. G. Flagon. H. Demijohn.

Sound Effects

1. A bird (an American nightjar). 2. Supersonic. 3. Bass. 4. A siren. 5. Loudly. 6. Rice Krispies. 7. The clapper. 8. Snoring. 9. A dog (hound). 10. Castanets.

General Quiz No. 7

1. John Lennon. 2. Lakes. 3. Mercury. 4. Bull. 5. Princess Anne. 6. A Bogeyman. 7. Veal. 8. The Muppets. 9. One. 10. Spices. 11. Peru. 12. Yeast. 13. Change colour. 14. Florida. 15. Marco. 16. A cygnet. 17. Airports. 18. Carpets. 19. Perseus. 20. A film actor.

Book Quiz

1. *Peter Rabbit* (by Beatrix Potter). 2. *Gulliver's Travels* (by Jonathan Swift). 3. *A Christmas Carol* (by Charles Dickens). 4. *Little Women* (by Louisa M. Alcott). 5. *The Water Babies* (by Charles Kingsley). 6. *Mary Poppins* (by P.L. Travers). 7. *Dracula* (by Bram Stoker). 8. *Ballet Shoes* (by Noel Streatfeild). 9. *Charlie and the Chocolate Factory* (by Roald Dahl). 10. *The Lion, the Witch and the Wardrobe* (by C.S. Lewis).

Picture Quiz — Find Your Feet

A. Trainers. B. Brogues. C. Mules. D. Flip-flops. E. Clogs. F. Galoshes. G. Moccasins.

General Quiz No. 8
1. Golf. 2. In St. Paul's Cathedral. 3. State Registered Nurse.
4. Snuff. 5. Guinness. 6. *Treasure Island* (by R.L. Stevenson).
7. Pouch. 8. A dance. 9. Ten. 10. Daffodils. 11. Hyde Park.
12. Beefeater. 13. Twenty-one. 14. A kind of fish. 15. Five
gold rings. 16. John Ross. 17. Qantas. 18. A lariat (or lasso).
19. In a quiver. 20. Chinese.

Picture Quiz — Look Sharp!
A. Billhook. B. Sickle. C. Adze. D. Axe. E. Scythe.
F. Drawshave. G. Shears. H. Ham knife. I. Chisel.
J. Machete. K. Jack knife. L. Bread knife. M. Pickaxe.
N. Cleaver.

General Quiz No. 9
1. Mr Magoo. 2. A snake. 3. Ice skating. 4. A nightingale.
5. Stratford-upon-Avon. 6. Ballerina. 7. Pharaoh. 8. The
choke. 9. A type of revolver. 10. Binary. 11. Buffalo.
12. Woman Police Constable. 13. On the shoulders. 14. An
Afghan hound. 15. Pasta. 16. *Jim'll Fix It*. 17. Seven.
18. Coral. 19. The Royal Albert Hall. 20. On the moon.

Picture Quiz — Panto Time
A. Sleeping Beauty. B. Aladdin. C. Red Riding Hood.
D. Dick Whittington. E. Cinderella. F. Ali Baba.

Great Names
1. Nelson. 2. Elvis Presley. 3. Cleopatra. 4. John Wayne.
5. Salome. 6. Adolf Hitler. 7. Edward VIII (The Duke of
Windsor). 8. Captain Scott. 9. Anne of Cleves. 10. Edgar
Allan Poe.

General Quiz No. 10
1. Egyptian. 2. Prisons. 3. A mime. 4. On a weather map. 5. A
stamped addressed envelope. 6. On a typewriter.
7. Gnasher. 8. A dried plum. 9. Capricorn. 10. Sir Walter
Raleigh. 11. Seventy. 12. Fencing. 13. At the beginning.
14. A type of sail. 15. Babylon. 16. The Vikings. 17. Roger
Hargreaves. 18. The mosquito. 19. Hare. 20. Edinburgh.

Ball Games
1. Two. 2. Baseball. 3. A mallet. 4. Cricket. 5. Handled.
6. Snooker. 7. Lacrosse. 8. Tottenham Hotspur. 9. A caddy.
10. Rugby.

Picture Quiz — Trademarks
A. Nelson. B. Florence Nightingale. C. Neptune.
D. Churchill. E. Robert the Bruce. F. King Alfred. G. Sherlock
Holmes.

General Quiz No. 11
1. A kind of knot. 2. Etcetera (Latin for "and so on"). 3. Dove.
4. Cooking. 5. A table. 6. Mulberry. 7. Cornwall. 8. *Gone
with the Wind.* 9. Charts. 10. A hat (tit for tat). 11. Twenty-five.
12. Diapers. 13. Types of seaweed. 14. The Knave.
15. Leonardo da Vinci. 16. Oval. 17. Percussion. 18. The
Golden Fleece. 19. The top. 20. Postman Pat.

Picture Quiz — All Birds
A. Pheasant. B. Grouse. C. Partridge. D. Ptarmigan. E. Quail.
F. Guinea Fowl. G. Wood Pigeon. A. Pelican. B. Herring
Gull. C. Stormy Petrel. D. Albatross. E. Cormorant.
F. Gannet. G. Puffin.

General Quiz No. 12
1. Shoes with very pointed toes. 2. Braille. 3. Sheffield. 4. In
Kensington Gardens. 5. A synagogue. 6. A church. 7. Hera.
8. The Pope. 9. Dachshund. 10. Ten. 11. Wales.
12. Mountains. 13. Red and white. 14. Figaro. 15. Toad-in-
the-hole. 16. Ark. 17. *Nein.* 18. Nine days. 19. Stamps.
20. Calcutta.

Picture Quiz — Little Beasts
A. Ermine. B. Marten. C. Skunk. D. Raccoon. E. Otter.
F. Mongoose.

Here and There
1. Japan. 2. Lancashire. 3. Dublin. 4. New York. 5. Arabia.
6. Sweden. 7. New Zealand. 8. Indies. 9. Camelot. 10. Africa.

General Quiz No. 13
1. A composer. 2. The metro. 3. Dizzy. 4. Quakers. 5. Storks.
6. Water. 7. Andrew Lloyd-Webber. 8. Athens. 9. Cliff
Richard. 10. At the Tower of London. 11. Above the ground.
(Though it looks like a sponge, it's the inside of a gourd.)
12. Jimmy Carter. 13. Bricks. 14. Deserts. 15. The Titanic.
16. A joey. 17. One thousand. 18. A famous Moscow soccer
team. 19. The wellington boot. 20. A breed of dog.

Stars and Planets
1. Mars. 2. The sun. 3. A bear (Ursa Major means Great
Bear). 4. Early astronauts. 5. Pluto. 6. The moon. 7. Very
cold. 8. Darth Vader. 9. Astronomy. 10. Venus.

Picture Quiz — Roots
A. Beetroot. B. Parsnip. C. Turnip. D. Radish. E. Carrot.
F. Ginger.

General Quiz No. 14
1. A bird. 2. Abba. 3. Almond. 4. Four. 5. Citizen's Band.
6. The Iron Cross. 7. Languages. 8. Four. 9. No smoking.
10. Leprechaun. 11. A tornado (or cyclone). 12. The rabbit.
13. A steam train. 14. Eat them (they're soused herrings).
15. Yacht racing. 16. The Pobble. 17. A prison sentence.
18. Alpha. 19. A log book. 20. Benjamin.

Picture Quiz — What Is It?
A. Anvil. B. Bassoon. C. Cameo. D. Dragonfly. E. Elf.
F. Frisbee. G. Gimlet. H. Hourglass. I. Ivy. J. Jodhpurs.
K. Kiwi. L. Limpet. M. Marrow.

General Quiz No. 15
1. A type of fruit. 2. *Play School.* 3. The black. 4. A circus.
5. The runt. 6. A coolabah. 7. A silo. 8. Tweety Pie. 9. 366.
10. Tap. 11. An ambassador. 12. Sea-sickness. 13. Royal
Ascot. 14. They were brothers. 15. Stanley. 16. The root.
17. Hermes. 18. Cricket. 19. A marionette. 20. Genesis.

Picture Quiz — Robes
A. Sari. B. Sarong. C. Kimono. D. Kaftan. E. Poncho.
F. Jellabah.

Eating Out
1. Indian. 2. Self-service. 3. A hamburger (or a steak).
4. Wine list. 5. Soy sauce. 6. On toast. 7. The chef. 8. Chips.
9. Italy. 10. Small.

General Quiz No. 16
1. The scut. 2. Queen Victoria. 3. A violin. 4. Sunday. 5. The
eyes. 6. Tight trousers. 7. Melon. 8. Danish. 9. A film actor.
10. Barrels. 11. Twelve. 12. Computers. 13. Heels.
14. Boxing. 15. A kind of tree. 16. Acting. 17. Knots. 18. His
strength. 19. A toby jug. 20. Red.

Page 68

Laughing Matters
1. Les Dawson. 2. Eric Morecambe. 3. Ball. 4. Little and Large. 5. Mike Yarwood. 6. Russ Abbot. 7. Bracket. 8. Emu. 9. The Goodies. 10. Tommy Cooper.

Page 69

Picture Quiz — All Lit Up
A. Chandelier. B. Japanese Lantern. C. Candelabra. D. Hurricane Lantern. E. Oil Lamp. F. Chinese Lantern. G. Sconce.

Page 70/71

General Quiz No. 17
1. Cotton. 2. A Bookmaker, or bookie. 3. J.R.R. Tolkein. 4. Vitamin C. 5. Goodbye. 6. Greenland. 7. Birds. 8. The trumpet. 9. A clove. 10. Knitting. 11. A kind of wig. 12. Chess. 13. A sealpoint. 14. Eric Bristow. 15. The Rovers' Return. 16. The Can-Can. 17. February 14th. 18. Charles I. 19. Love. 20. The Pied Piper of Hamelin.

Page 72/73

Picture Quiz — What Is It? (Part 2)
N. Nosebag. O. Orchid. P. Palm. Q. Quill. R. Raft. S. Spanner. T. Trellis. U. Uniform. V. Vampire. W. Walrus. X. Xylophone. Y. Yacht. Z. Zebra.

General Quiz No. 18
1. Wendy Craig. 2. The National Savings Bank. 3. In the garden. 4. France. 5. A scald. 6. Margaret Thatcher (who became Britain's first woman Prime Minister). 7. Five rings, interlinked. 8. Minnehaha ("Laughing Water"). 9. Boadicea (also called Boudicca). 10. High jumping. 11. Three. 12. Mahatma Gandhi. 13. The Nile. 14. Bobby Shafto. 15. Clotted cream. 16. 1953. 17. A gorilla. 18. Julius Caesar. 19. Leather. 20. The "William" books (by Richmal Crompton).

Picture Quiz — Sounds of the Past
A. Lyre. B. Lute. C. Banjo. D. Sackbut. E. Post horn. F. Dulcimer.

Horses and Ponies
1. Shetland (a pony— the others are heavy horses). 2. On its leg. 3. Pegasus. 4. He painted them. 5. A colt. 6. A groom (at an inn). 7. *Black Beauty*. 8. A palomino. 9. The Grand National. 10. Mule.

General Quiz No. 19
1. A whale (in the book by Herman Melville). 2. Anglesey. 3. Catherine of Aragon. 4. Ill. 5. H.G. Wells. 6. A turn. 7. Twenty-one. 8. The Panama Canal. 9. A sheep. 10. Polly. 11. Open spaces. 12. Your Grace. 13. Spain. 14. Nautilus. 15. Railway stations. 16. A hill. 17. Perambulator. 18. Hotels. 19. Beethoven. 20. Show Jumping.

Page 80

Threesomes
1. All Prime Ministers. 2. All tennis players. 3. All apples. 4. All writers (novelists). 5. All beheaded. 6. All runners.
7. All rivers. 8. All artists. 9. All types of computer. 10. All pop-singers.

Page 81

Picture Quiz — Teatime
A. Eccles cake. B. Eclair. C. Swiss roll. D. Victoria sponge.
E. Battenburg. F. Doughnut.

Page 82/83

General Quiz No. 20
1. Monaco. 2. A holt. 3. Haggis. 4. The liver. 5. Sculpture.
6. A type of fruit. 7. The Egyptians. 8. Types of cloud.
9. Motor racing. 10. I serve. (The motto is in German).
11. *Watership Down* (by Richard Adams). 12. Campaign for Nuclear Disarmament. 13. Arthur C. Clarke. 14. Five.
15. Girls' public schools. 16. Vesuvius. 17. Cardinal Wolsey.
18. Lieutenant-General. 19. His mother. 20. St. George's.

Page 84/85

Picture Quiz — Take a Seat
A. Ladderback. B. Chaise Longue. C. Windsor. D. Wing.
E. Corner. F. Basket. G. Chippendale. H. Settee. I. Porter's.
J. Love seat. K. Buttonback. L. Throne.

General Quiz No. 21
1. Hindu gods. 2. A hairstyle. 3. Batik. 4. Captain Cook.
5. 1877. 6. China. 7. Witches. 8. The Scarlet Pimpernel.
9. Vivaldi. 10. A Chief Petty Officer. 11. Bridge. 12. Magnus
Magnusson. 13. Skiing. 14. A leak. 15. Karl Marx.
16. Violoncello. 17. Needles. 18. Poland. 19. Your birthday.
20. Leonid.

Picture Quiz — Creepy-Crawlies
A. June bug. B. Earwig. C. Ladybird. D. Cockroach. E. Stag
beetle. F. Colorado beetle.

Crime and Detection
1. Sherlock Holmes. 2. Ripper. 3. Kojak. 4. Agatha Christie.
5. *The Pink Panther*. 6. The sparrow. 7. *Oliver Twist*.
8. Into the witness box. 9. London. 10. He stabbed him.

General Quiz No. 22
1. It grows a new one. 2. Archimedes. 3. Tobago. 4. Stand.
5. Aintree. 6. Chequers. 7. Table tennis. 8. General Custer.
9. Marchioness. 10. Ballet. 11. A kind of monkey. 12. 28.
13. Tanks. 14. On Her Majesty's Service. 15. 174.
16. Insects. 17. John Milton. 18. A gavel. 19. Green.
20. Whalebone.

Sleepyheads
1. Little Boy Blue. 2. Rip Van Winkle. 3. Siesta. 4. Joseph.
5. "All through the night." 6. Forty. 7. Policeman. 8. His
nightgown. 9. William Shakespeare. 10. Hibernate.

Picture Quiz — Marine Life
A. Sperm Whale. B. Dugong. C. Porpoise. D. Killer Whale.
E. Dolphin. F. Walrus.

General Quiz No. 23
1. A bat. 2. Tapioca. 3. Acoustics. 4. Willcox. 5. Black hole.
6. It could talk. 7. Prawns. 8. A pocket watch. 9. Macramé.
10. Fish-like. 11. Geometry. 12. The Koran. 13. Ministry of
Transport. 14. Kabul. 15. Northern Ireland. 16. A
high-ranking official — often military. 17. Stephen.
18. A fracture. 19. At six o'clock. 20. Bing Crosby.

Picture Quiz — Bigwigs
A. Grandee. B. Mogul. C. Shah. D. Sultan. E. Rajah.
F. Mandarin. G. Pharaoh. H. Kaiser. I. Shogun. J. Tsar.

General Quiz No. 24
1. Loudspeakers. 2. Jupiter. 3. Greek. 4. Tintoretto.
5. Woman. 6. The Archbishop of Canterbury. 7. Branwell
Brontë. 8. Round. 9. Vertical takeoff and landing. 10. A fish.
11. Hadrian's Wall. 12. Tapestry. 13. Roger Bannister.
14. Thermals. 15. Crying. 16. Bangladesh. 17. Tightrope
walking. 18. Versus (Latin for "against"). 19. Bald.
20. Democrats.

Page 100

Famous Dogs

1. A collie. 2. *The Wizard of Oz*. 3. Nana. 4. Snoopy. 5. *Blue Peter*. 6. The Queen. 7. Dougal. 8. *Hart to Hart*. 9. *Lady and the Tramp*. 10. Timmy.

Page 101

Boats

1. An owl. 2. The Thames. 3. An insect. 4. Ratty (The Water Rat). 5. Straw. 6. Lifeboat Institution. 7. On a canal. 8. Eton. 9. The oars. 10. Venice.

Page 102/103

General Quiz No. 25

1. Frances Hodgson Burnett. 2. On the Orkney Islands. 3. An angler. (They are types of artificial fly.) 4. Nail.
5. Ambidextrous. 6. Computer. 7. Disguise.
8. 20. 9. Earl Mountbatten of Burma. 10. Fiji. 11. Tyburn.
12. Lawn tennis. 13. Hungarian. 14. Israel. 15. On a barrow.
16. "The Road to the Isles." 17. The Rev. Dr. Spooner (after whom "Spoonerisms" take their name). 18. Dionne Warwick. 19. Schoolmaster. 20. Marilyn Monroe.

Page 104

Monsters

1. One. 2. The Abominable Snowman. 3. Frankenstein.
4. King Kong. 5. Snakes. 6. The Loch Ness Monster.
7. Beowulf. 8. A dinosaur. 9. Mr. Hyde. 10. Bull.

THE EVEN MORE AWFUL JOKE BOOK

Compiled by Mary Danby

It's worse than ever!

Drive your family and friends up the wall with this fantastic new collection of glorious groaners, rib-tickling riddles, horrendous howlers and crazy cartoons. Here are a few sickly samples to whet your appetite . . .

Did you hear about the lady who wired up her electric blanket to a toaster?
She kept popping out of bed all night.

JIMMY: I'm sorry I'm late, sir, but I was having a dream about a football match.
TEACHER: Why did that make you late?
JIMMY: They played extra time.

Why did the wagon train stop in the middle of the prairie?
It had Injun trouble.

Armada

Kay Tracey Mysteries
by Frances K. Judd

Look out for Armada's fantastic new detective series!

Kay Tracey has an uncanny talent for solving clues and unravelling baffling mysteries. Don't miss her first two thrilling adventures.

> 1 The Double Disguise
> 2 In the Sunken Garden

Armada

THE MILLIONAIRE'S HANDBOOK
Peter Eldin

A treasure-trove of money-making schemes . . .

Cash-in on –

Car-washing
Budget-planning
House-minding
Bait-breeding
Bulb-growing

and many more ideas for getting rich quick. It'll be your best-ever investment!

Armada

LINDA CRAIG
MYSTERIES

by ANN SHELDON

Now there's a thrilling new mystery series in Armada:

Linda Craig loves horses – and adventure! Together, she and her beautiful palomino pony, Chica d'Oro, find themselves caught up in all kinds of dangerous escapades – chasing cut-throat horse thieves through underground caverns, roaring down mountain passes after death-dealing smugglers, treasure-hunting in the burning desert – and much more. Make sure you don't miss Linda's action-packed adventures.

If you like Nancy Drew, you'll love Linda Craig!

Armada

MILL GREEN

School Series

by *Alison Prince*

Now there's a great new school series in Armada.

Mill Green is a big, new comprehensive – with more than its fair share of dramas and disasters! Get to know Matt, Danny, Rachel, and the rest of the First Form mob in their first two exciting adventures.

Mill Green on Fire

When someone starts fires in the school and blames the caretaker, Matt is determined to catch the real culprit. But his brilliant plan to catch the firebug goes horribly wrong . . .

Mill Green on Stage

The First Formers prepare for the Christmas pantomime – and sparks soon fly when Marcia Mudd, a ghastly new girl, gets the best part. But when Matt locks Marcia in a cupboard and she disappears from the school, there's big trouble for everyone . . .

A Spy at Mill Green

The school is stunned when its brand-new video recorder and television camera are stolen. With all the clues pointing to an inside job, the First Formers turn detective . . .

More stories about Mill Green will be published in Armada.

Armada

SUPERSLEUTHS

by FRANKLIN W. DIXON and CAROLYN KEENE

A feast of reading for all mystery fans!

At last, the Hardy Boys and Nancy Drew have joined forces to become the world's most brilliant detective team!

Together, the daredevil sleuths investigate seven spine-chilling mysteries: a deadly roller-coaster that hurtles to disaster, a sinister bell that tolls in a city of skeletons, a haunted opera house with a sinister curse — and many more terrifying situations.

Nancy Drew and the Hardy Boys — *dynamite!*

Armada

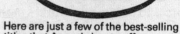

HI KIDS! I'VE GOT THE POWER TO BRING YOU FUN, ADVENTURE, AND EXCITEMENT!

Here are just a few of the best-selling titles that Armada has to offer:

- ☐ **Ride Like the Wind** Patricia Leitch 95p
- ☐ **The Wind in the Willows** Kenneth Grahame £1.25
- ☐ **The Treasure Hunters** Enid Blyton 85p
- ☐ **The Viking Symbol Mystery** Franklin W. Dixon 95p
- ☐ **Biggles Hunts Big Game** Captain W. E. Johns 95p
- ☐ **The Hidden Staircase** Carolyn Keene 95p
- ☐ **The Ghost Town Treasure** Ann Sheldon 95p
- ☐ **Mill Green on Stage** Alison Prince 95p
- ☐ **The Mystery of Shark Reef** Alfred Hitchcock 95p
- ☐ **The Dukes of Hazzard: Gone Racin'** Eric Alter 95p
- ☐ **The Chalet School Fete** Elinor M. Brent-Dyer 95p

Armadas are available in bookshops and newsagents, but can also be ordered by post.

HOW TO ORDER
ARMADA BOOKS, Cash Sales Dept., GPO Box 29, Douglas, Isle of Man, British Isles. Please send purchase price of book plus postage, as follows:—

    1—4 Books . . . . 10p per copy
    5 Books or more . . . no further charge
    25 Books sent post free within U.K.

Overseas Customers: 12p per copy.

NAME (Block letters) _____

ADDRESS _____

_____

_____